ALL OCCASION PAGES

ILLUSTRATED FILL-IN SKILL ACTIVITY SHEETS

BY BEVERLY ARMSTRONG

The Learning Works

To the Teacher

If you have students with special needs, if you want to individualize instruction but don't have time, or if you have creative ideas but have never developed your artistic talent, this book is for you. The ready-to-use art on its **All Occasion Pages** reflects holiday and seasonal themes. There are apples, pilgrims' hats, turkeys, Santa's sacks, snowmen, Lincoln's logs, hearts, kites, bunnies, and many more fun and festive shapes.

You supply the subject matter and turn these pages into custom-made activity sheets to present, review, or reinforce a skill at any grade or interest level. For example, you might write math problems or spelling or vocabulary words in the numbered seasonal shapes. Or you might reproduce and hand out a page of blank shapes and encourage students to fill them in with problems for others to work or with words they have chosen to learn.

The sheets may also be used as game boards or game cards, or to help students keep track of their progress. Using a broad-tipped marking pen, you might connect the shapes in numerical order and mark the first **start** and the last **finish** to turn one sheet into a board for a follow-the-trail game. Simply indicate what rules students are to follow or what independent tasks they must complete to move from beginning to end. Or use a page for a bingo-style find, match, and cover game.

These pages of numbered seasonal shapes are also ideal for reading readiness practice, following directions activities, and art projects. In fact, once the book is yours, you'll think of many other uses for its **All Occasion Pages** and wonder how you ever did without them!

Copyright © 1982
THE LEARNING WORKS, INC.
Santa Barbara, CA 93111
All rights reserved.
Printed in the United States of America.

Name _____

Lots of Leaves

Name _____

Ships for Columbus

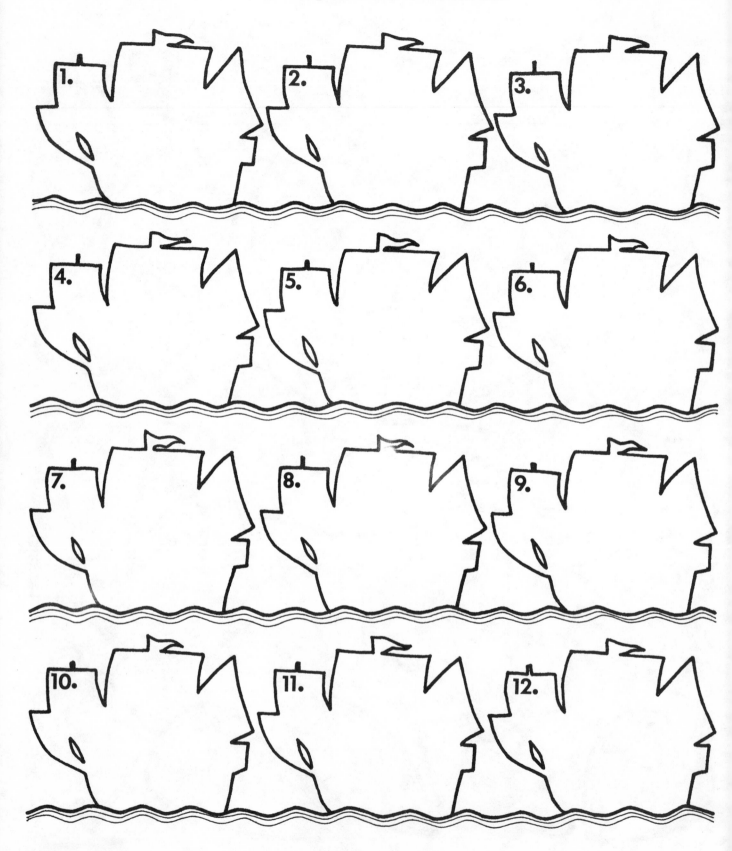

Hibernation Harvest

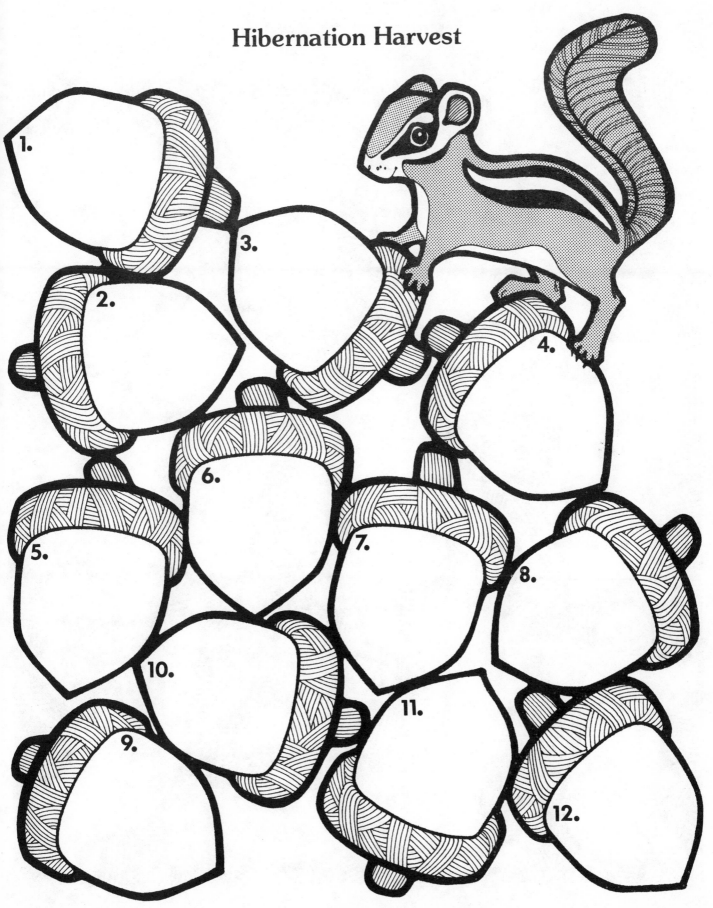

Floating Ghosts

8

Pumpkin Party

1.   2.   3.   4.
5.   6.   7.   8.
9.   10.   11.   12.
13.   14.   15.   16.

Trick or Treats

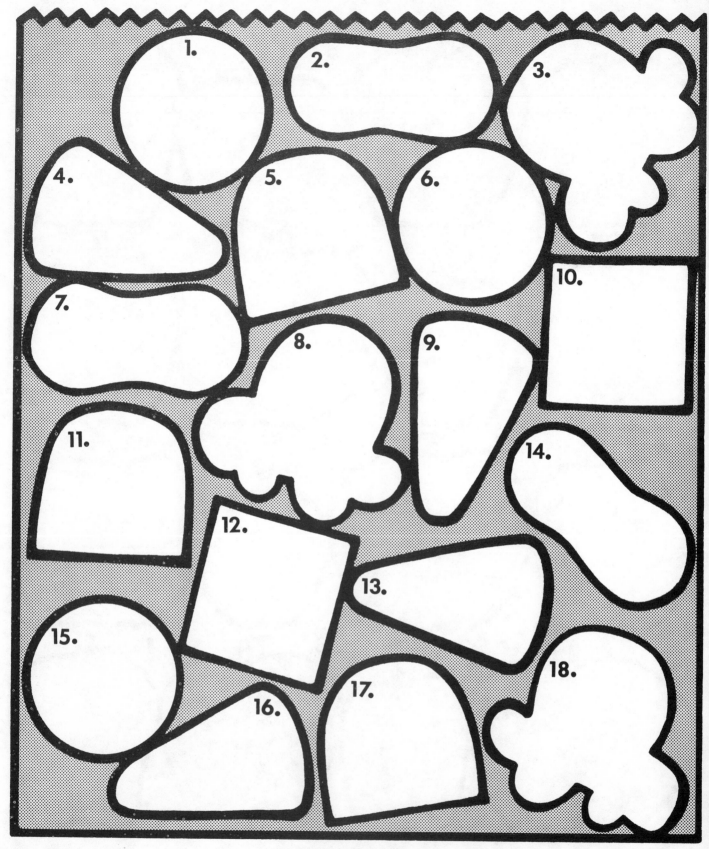

Turkey Trot

Pilgrim Problems

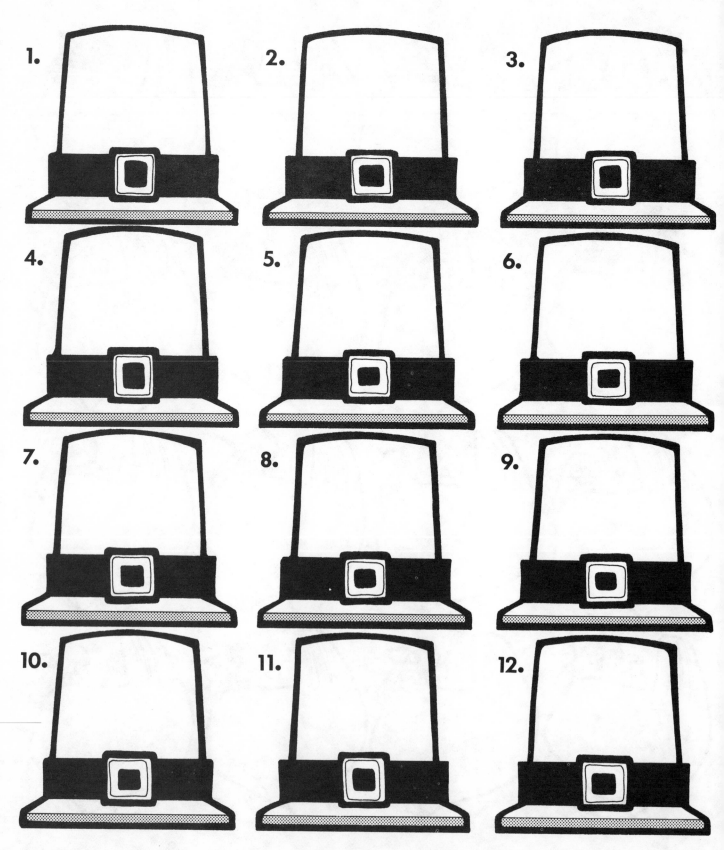

Santa's Sacks

Candlelight Delight

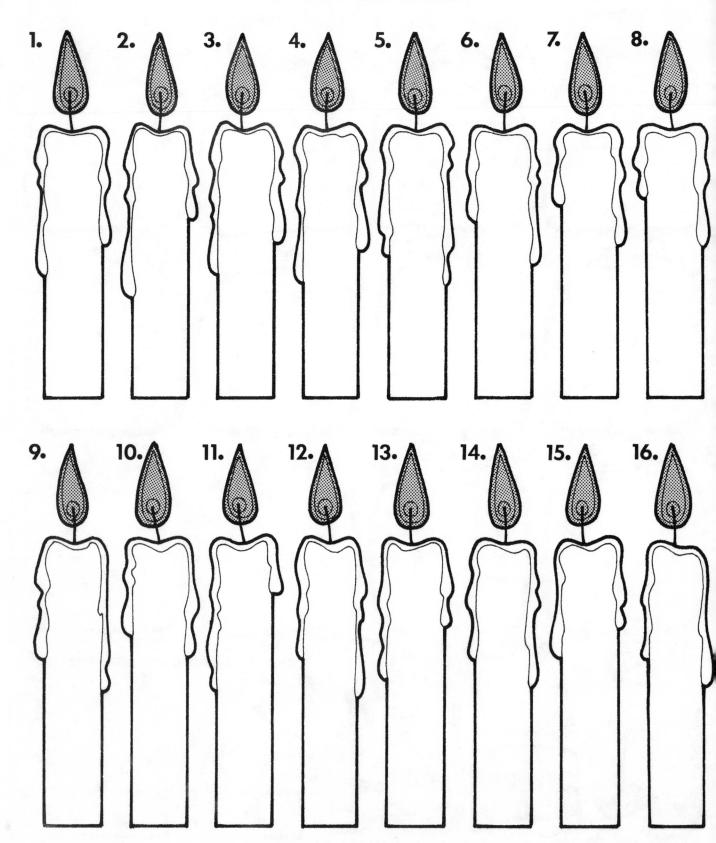

1. 2. 3. 4. 5. 6. 7. 8.

9. 10. 11. 12. 13. 14. 15. 16.

Pick a Package

Snowflake Fun

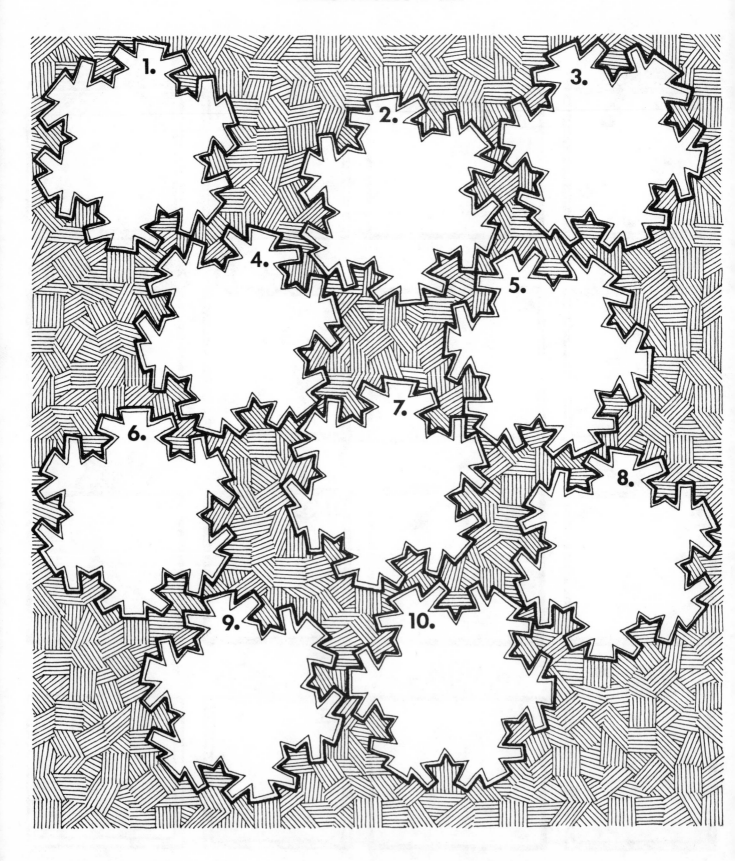

Happy New Year Hats

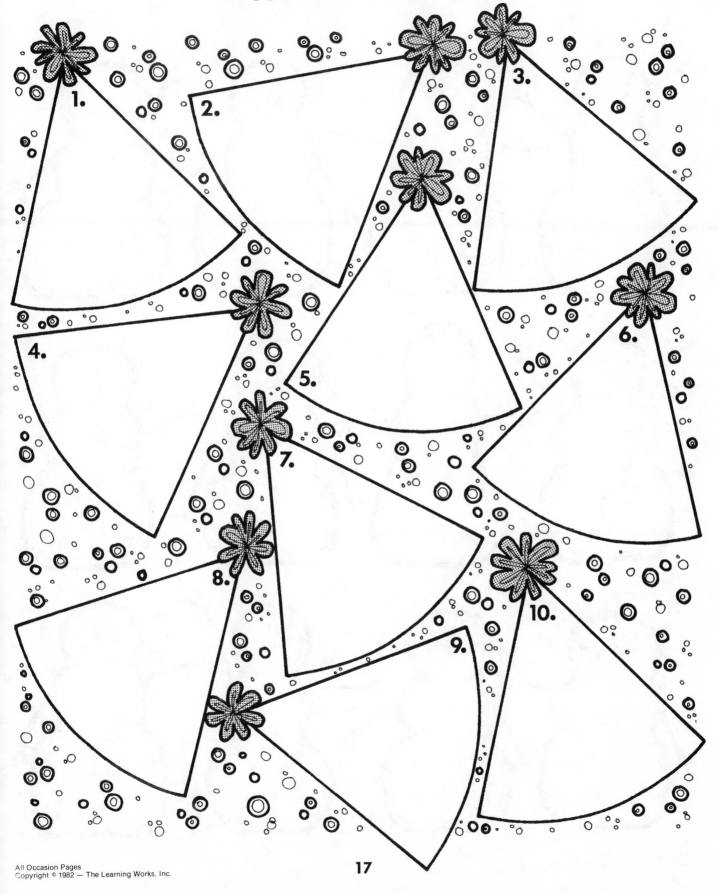

Name _____

Silly Snowmen

Ice Is Nice

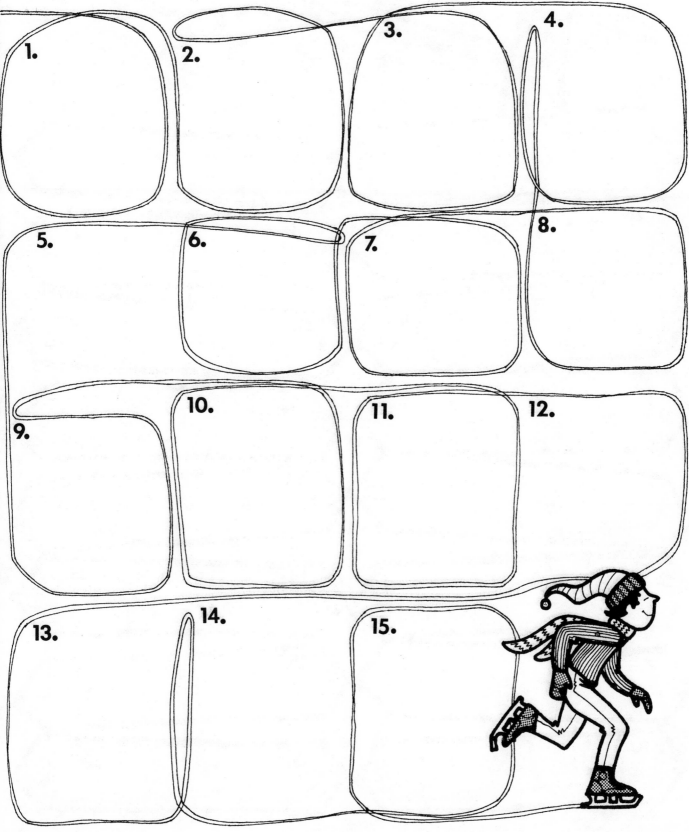

1.

2.

3.

4.

5.

6.

7.

8.

9.

10.

11.

12.

13.

14.

15.

Lincoln's Logs

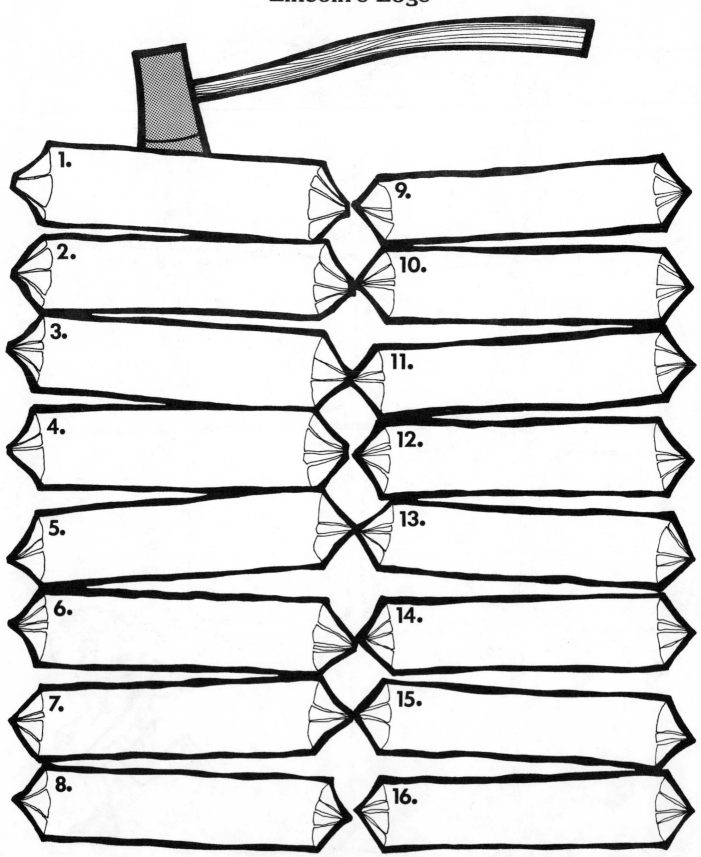

1.

2.

3.

4.

5.

6.

7.

8.

9.

10.

11.

12.

13.

14.

15.

16.

NaNName _____

Have a Heart

February Cherries

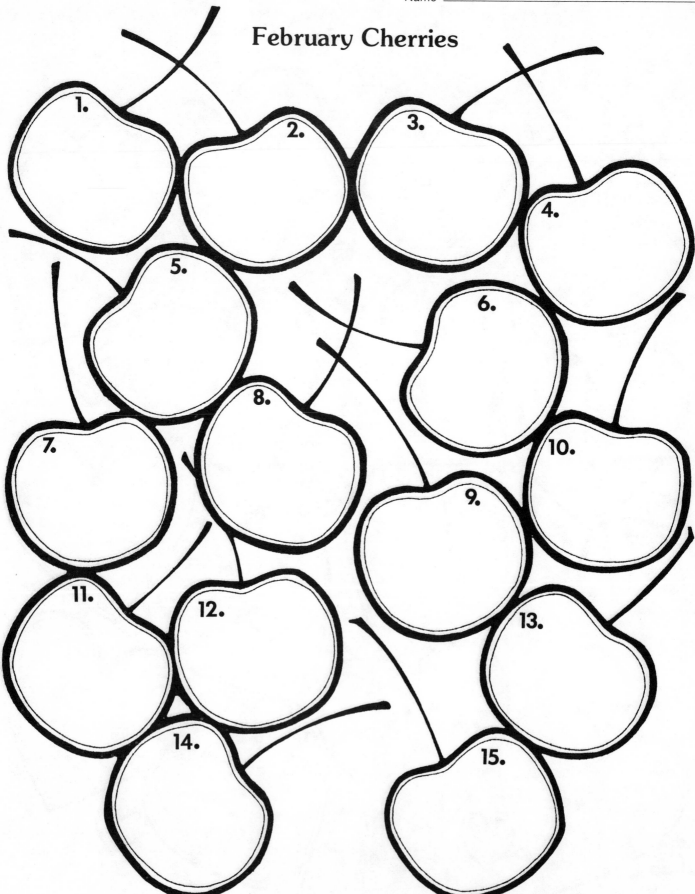

22

Name _____

Lucky Shamrocks

Kite Flight

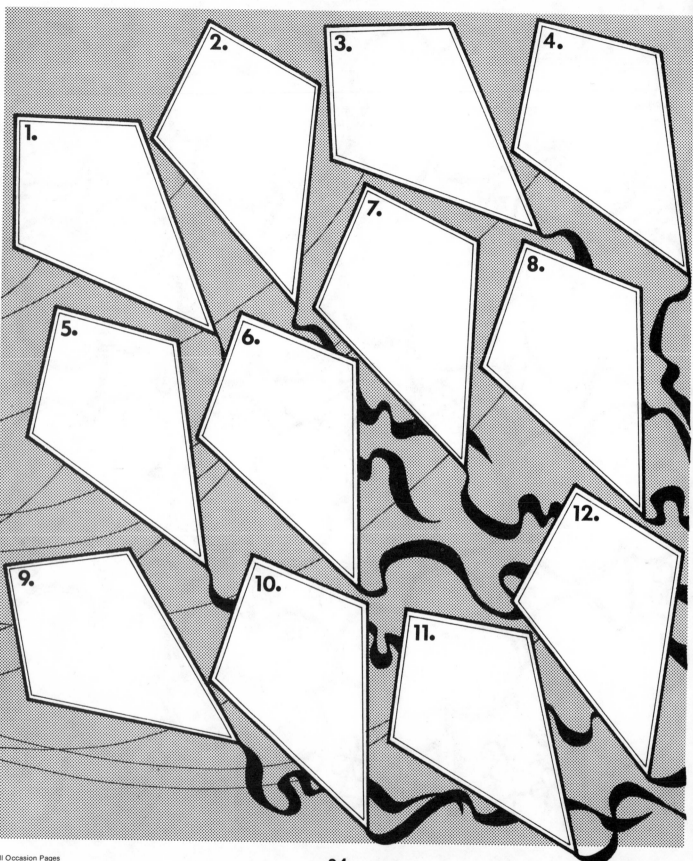

April Showers

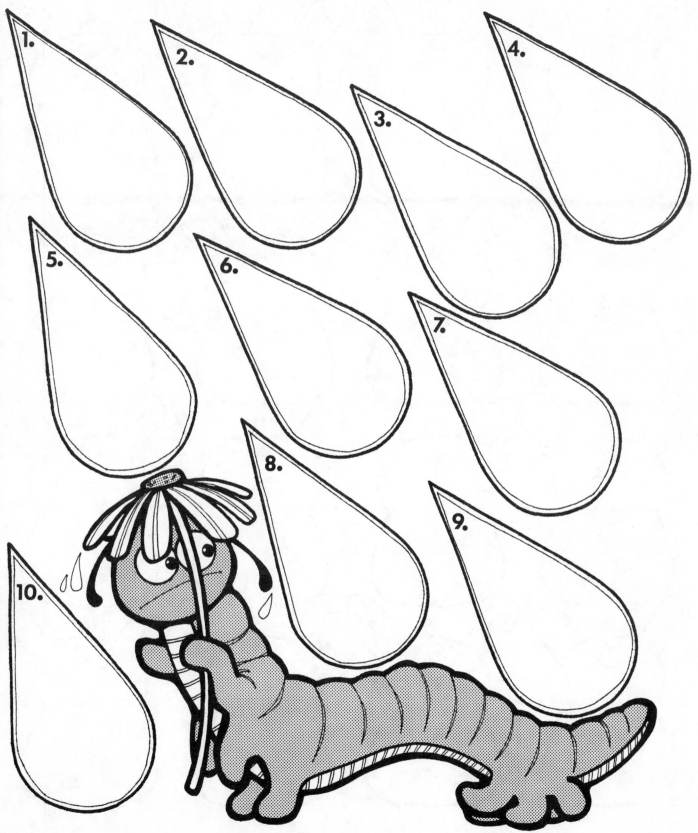

Funny Bunnies

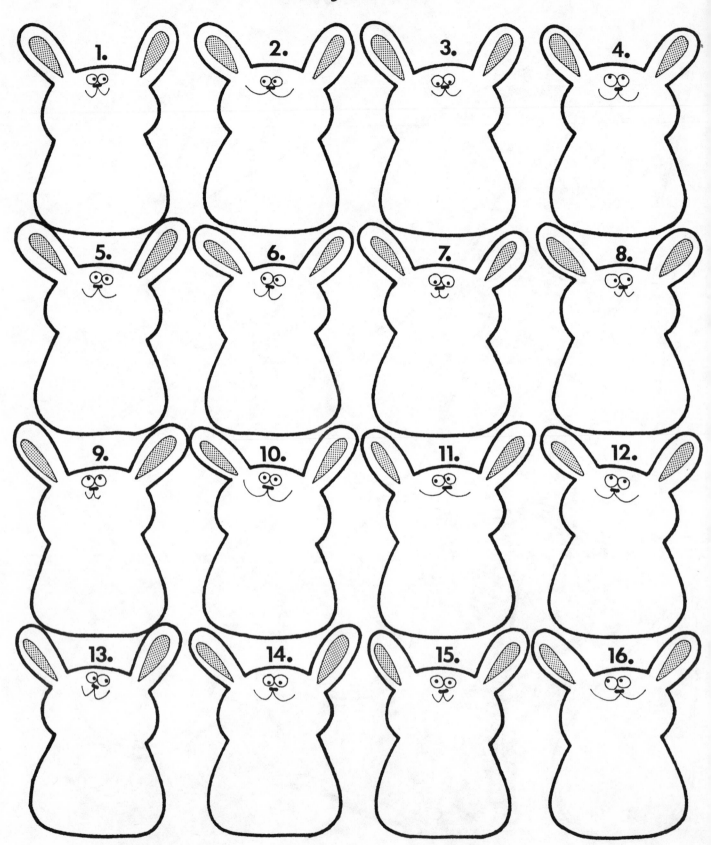

Name _____

A Dozen Eggs

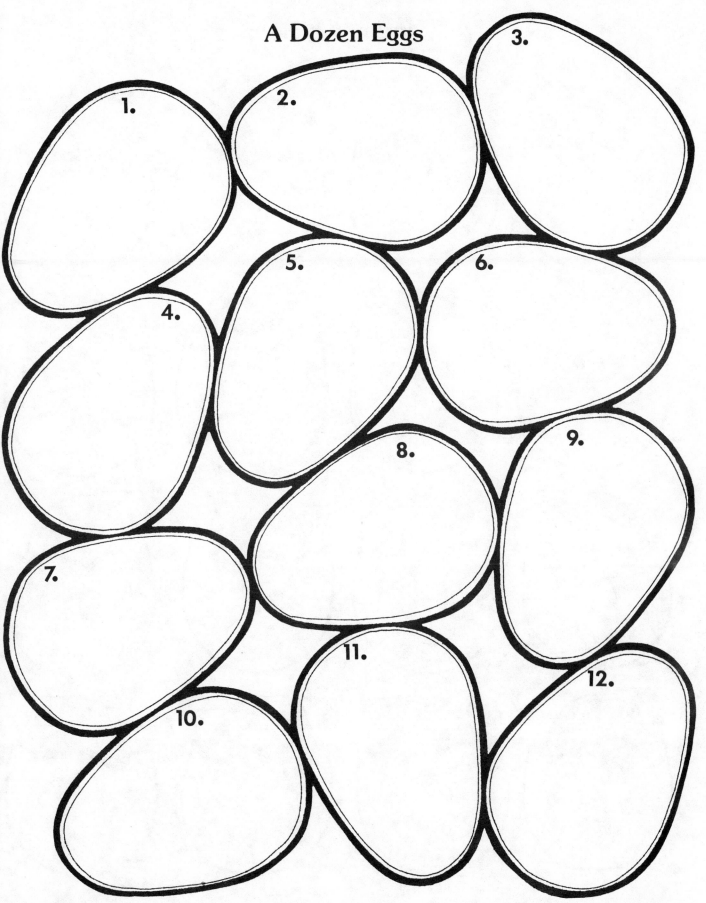

Spring Chickens

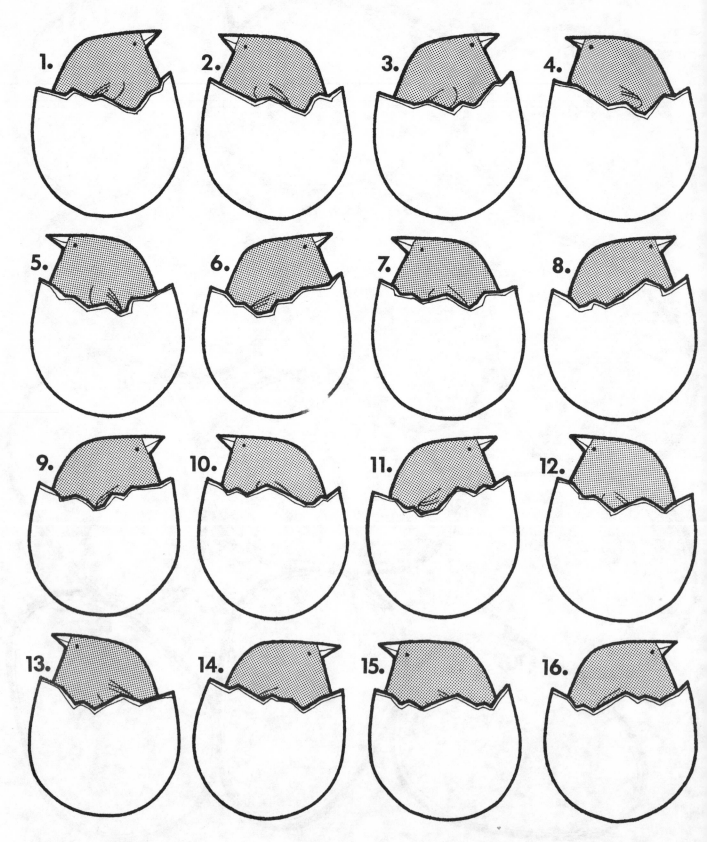

Name _____

May Daisies

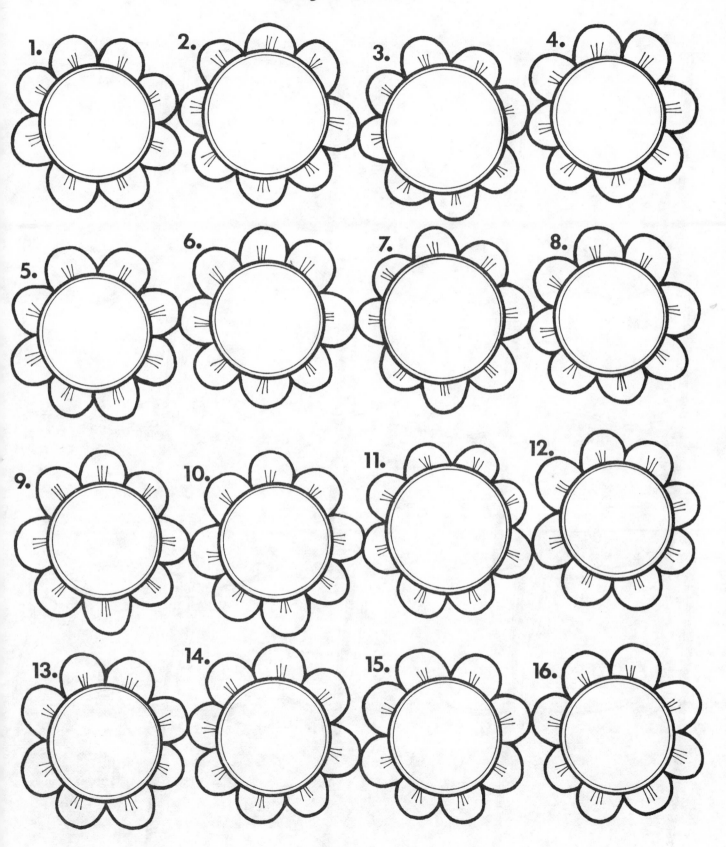

Flying Flags

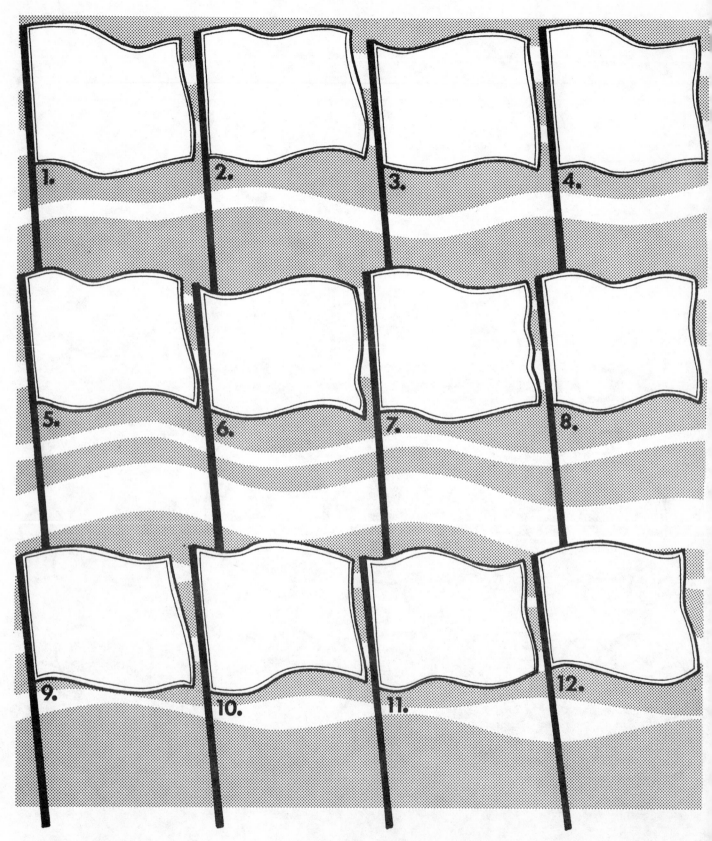

Summer Suns

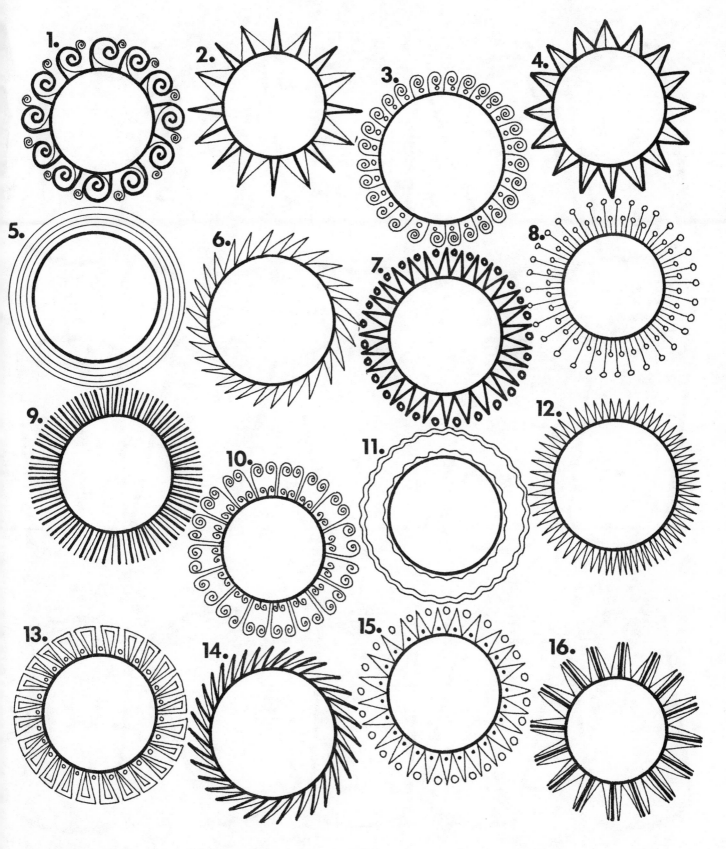

Light a Firecracker

Name _____